Handwriting Practice Book for Kids

Belongs to:

_____

Ages 6-8: Printing workbook for Grades 1, 2 & 3,
Learn to Trace Alphabet Letters and Numbers 1-100, Sight Words, 101 Jokes
Improve writing penmanship

This is a beginning handwriting book that helps kids learn or improve their writing in a fun and easy way.

Loads of cheerful and interesting illustrations will encourage kids to use this workbook.

It is organized in a progressively skill building way for kids to develop confidence to write neatly and improve penmanship.

Part 1: Learning the Alphabet:
Trace and practice letters a-z and A-Z

Part 2: Writing Sight Words

Part 3: Writing Numbers & Number Words from 1 - 100

Part 4: Writing Knock Knock Jokes in a smaller letter size

Part 5: Writing Jokes

You can use a pencil or pen to trace the dotted letters, numbers, words and jokes.

Meet Jojo.
Jojo is a curious elephant.
He loves to learn and play.
Learn to write along with Jojo!

Hi!
My name is Sujatha Lalgudi. I sincerely hope you find my handwriting book to be helpful and fun.

Write to me at **sujatha.lalgudi@gmail.com** with the subject:

Trace Grade along with **your kid's name** to receive:

- Additional practice worksheets.
- A name tracing worksheet so your kid can practice writing their own name.
- An Award Certificate in Color to gift your child!

If you liked this book, please leave me a review on Amazon! Your kind reviews and comments will encourage me to make more books like this.

Thank you
Sujatha Lalgudi

Part 1:
Learning the Alphabet

Trace the uppercase and lowercase letters and practice writing them on your own in the remaining space!

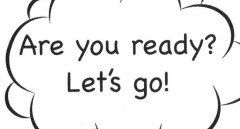

Are you ready?
Let's go!

A A A A

A A A A

A

1 /A\ 2
3

2 (a) 4
3

a a a a

a a a a

a

Aa Bb Cc Dd Ee Ff Gg Hh Ii Jj Kk Ll Mm Nn Oo Pp Qq Rr Ss Tt Uu Vv Ww Xx Yy Zz

B

1 ↓ B)2)3

B   B   B   B

B   B   B   B

B

b

1↓ 2 3

b   b   b   b

b   b   b   b

b

Aa Bb Cc Dd Ee Ff Gg Hh Ii Jj Kk Ll Mm Nn Oo Pp Qq Rr Ss Tt Uu Vv Ww Xx Yy Zz

C   C   C   C   C

C   C   C   C

C

C   C   C   C

C   C   C   C

C

Trace the letters, then write your own.   Name: Date:

D   D   D   D   D

D   D   D   D

D

d   d   d   d

d   d   d   d

d

E

e

Aa Bb Cc Dd Ee Ff Gg Hh Ii Jj Kk Ll Mm Nn Oo Pp Qq Rr Ss Tt Uu Vv Ww Xx Yy Zz

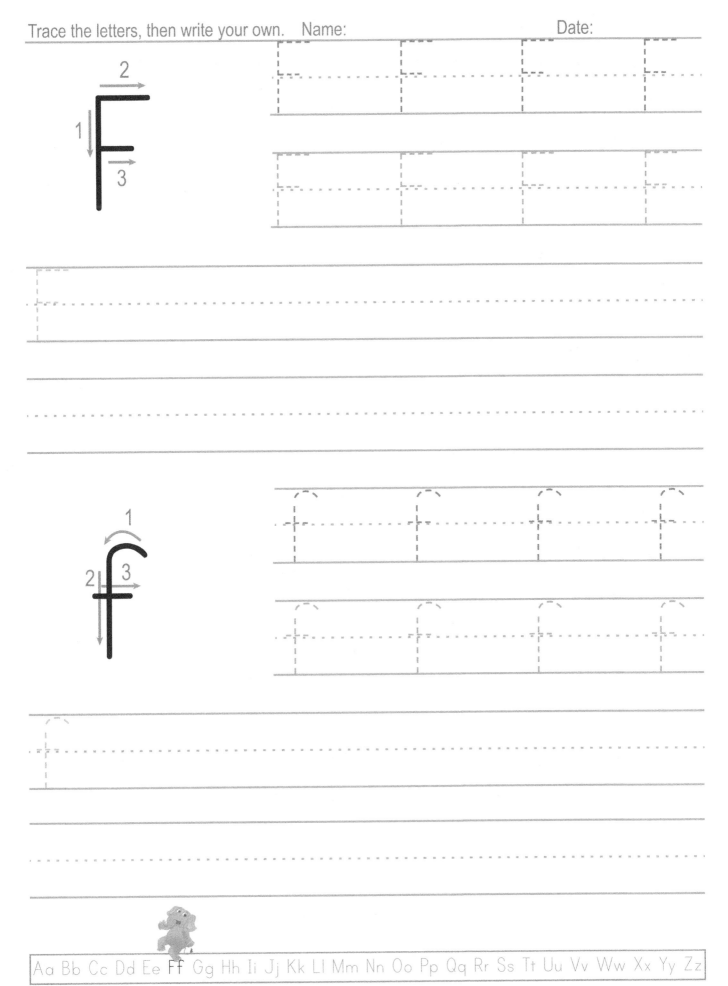

Aa Bb Cc Dd Ee Ff Gg Hh Ii Jj Kk Ll Mm Nn Oo Pp Qq Rr Ss Tt Uu Vv Ww Xx Yy Zz

G   G   G   G

G   G   G   G

G

g   g   g   g

g   g   g   g

g

Aa Bb Cc Dd Ee Ff **Gg** Hh Ii Jj Kk Ll Mm Nn Oo Pp Qq Rr Ss Tt Uu Vv Ww Xx Yy Zz

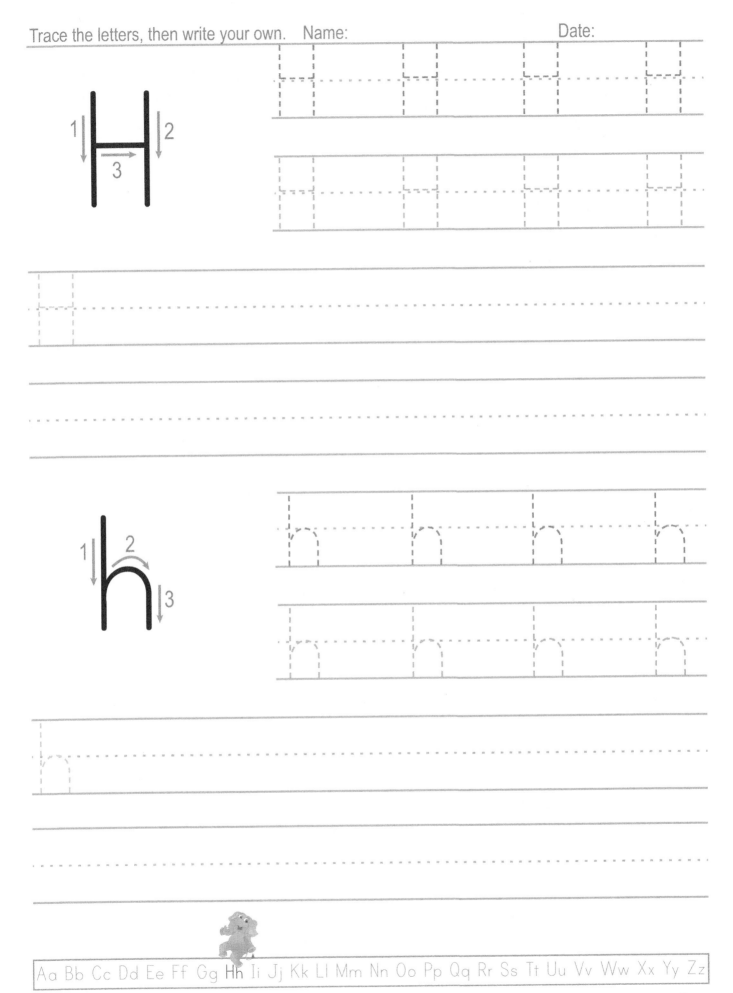

Aa Bb Cc Dd Ee Ff Gg Hh Ii Jj Kk Ll Mm Nn Oo Pp Qq Rr Ss Tt Uu Vv Ww Xx Yy Zz

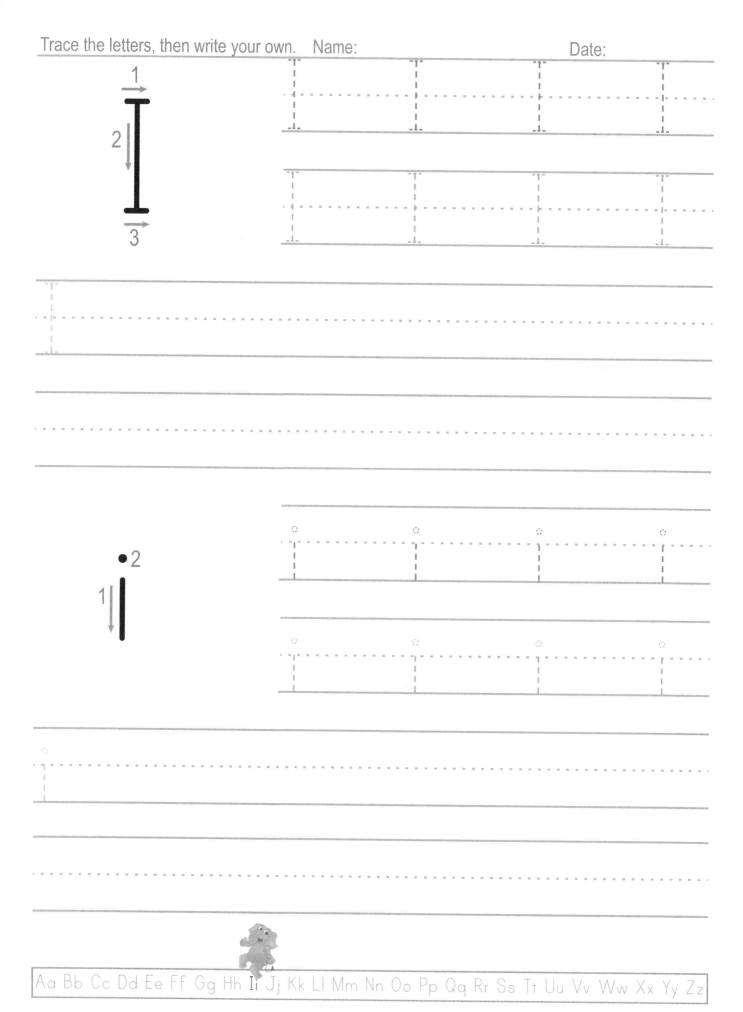

Aa Bb Cc Dd Ee Ff Gg Hh Ii Jj Kk Ll Mm Nn Oo Pp Qq Rr Ss Tt Uu Vv Ww Xx Yy Zz

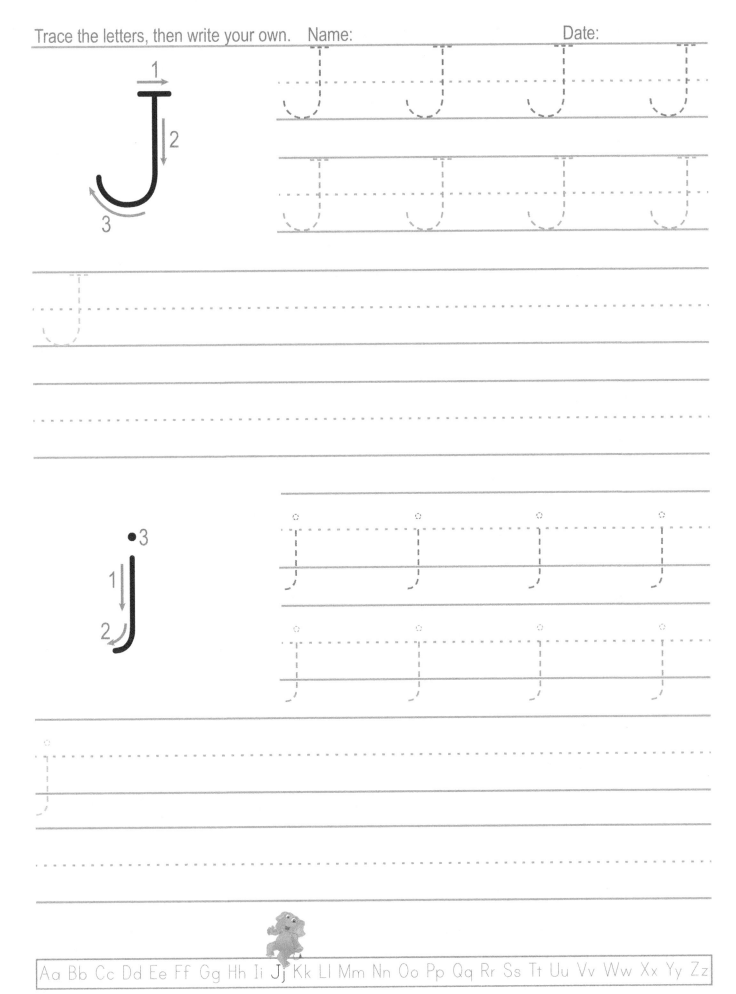

Aa Bb Cc Dd Ee Ff Gg Hh Ii Jj Kk Ll Mm Nn Oo Pp Qq Rr Ss Tt Uu Vv Ww Xx Yy Zz

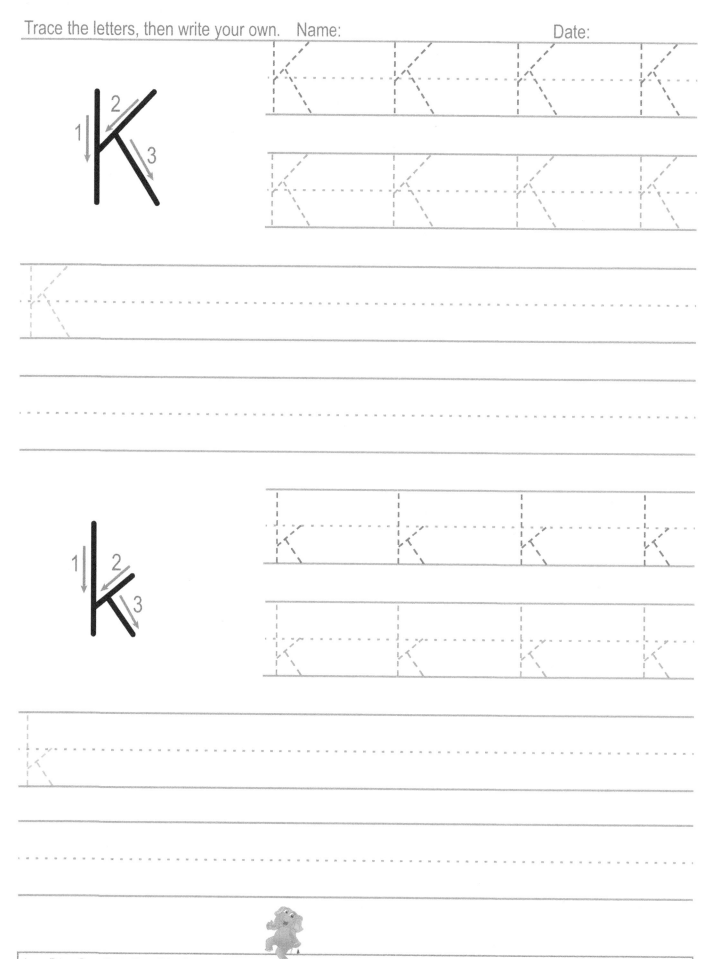

Aa Bb Cc Dd Ee Ff Gg Hh Ii Jj Kk Ll Mm Nn Oo Pp Qq Rr Ss Tt Uu Vv Ww Xx Yy Zz

Trace the letters, then write your own.   Name: _____   Date: _____

L

1↓ 2→

I

1↓

A a B b C c D d E e F f G g H h I i J j K k L l M m N n O o P p Q q R r S s T t U u V v W w X x Y y Z z

Trace the letters, then write your own.   Name: Date:

M

m

N　N　N　N

N　N　N　N

n　n　n　n

n　n　n　n

Aa Bb Cc Dd Ee Ff Gg Hh Ii Jj Kk Ll Mm Nn Oo Pp Qq Rr Ss Tt Uu Vv Ww Xx Yy Zz

Trace the letters, then write your own.   Name: _____   Date: _____

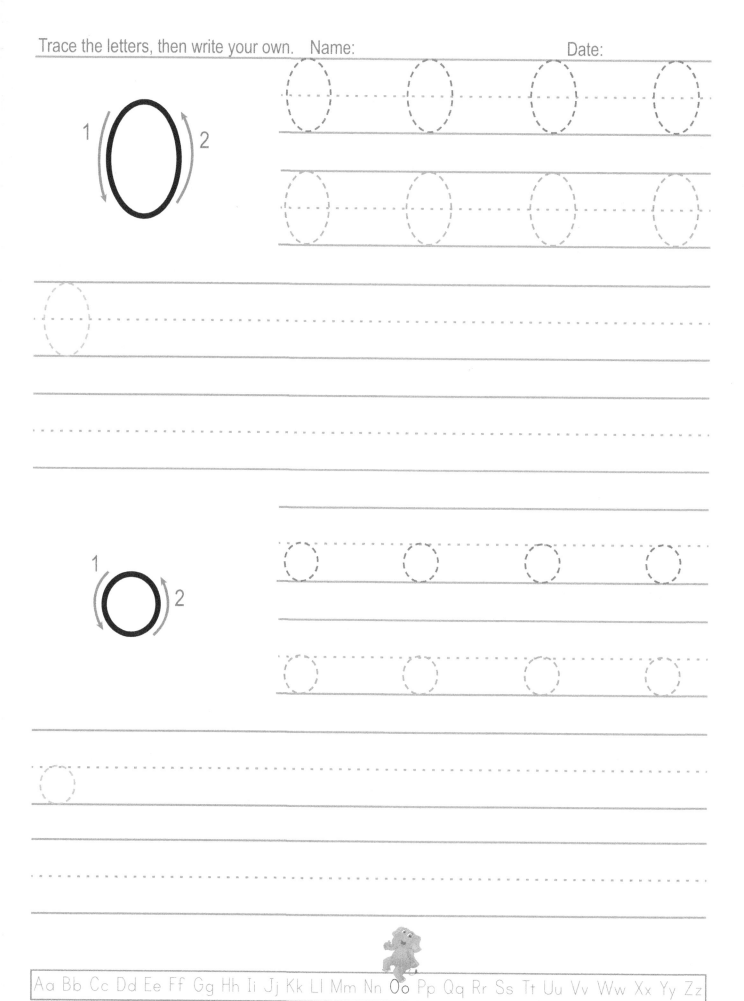

Aa Bb Cc Dd Ee Ff Gg Hh Ii Jj Kk Ll Mm Nn Oo Pp Qq Rr Ss Tt Uu Vv Ww Xx Yy Zz

Trace the letters, then write your own.   Name: Date:

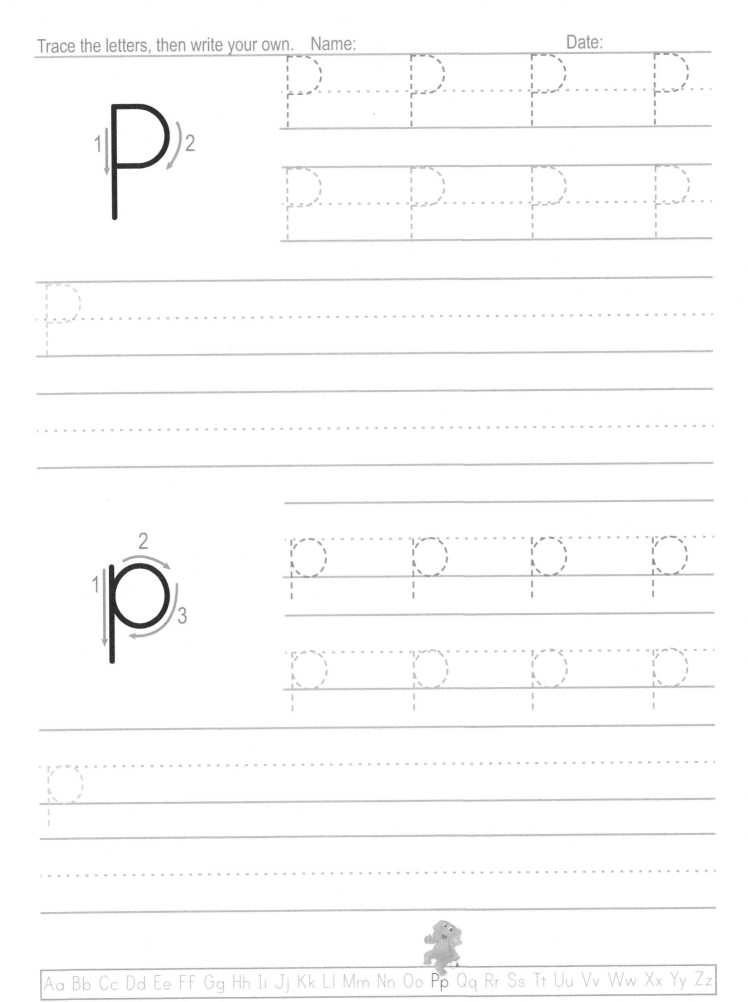

Aa Bb Cc Dd Ee Ff Gg Hh Ii Jj Kk Ll Mm Nn Oo Pp Qq Rr Ss Tt Uu Vv Ww Xx Yy Zz

Q

1 2 3

q

1 3 2

Aa Bb Cc Dd Ee Ff Gg Hh Ii Jj Kk Ll Mm Nn Oo Pp Qq Rr Ss Tt Uu Vv Ww Xx Yy Zz

Trace the letters, then write your own. Name: Date:

R

Rr

Aa Bb Cc Dd Ee Ff Gg Hh Ii Jj Kk Ll Mm Nn Oo Pp Qq **Rr** Ss Tt Uu Vv Ww Xx Yy Zz

S   S   S   S   S

S   S   S   S

S

S
1
2

S   S   S   S

S   S   S   S

S

Aa Bb Cc Dd Ee Ff Gg Hh Ii Jj Kk Ll Mm Nn Oo Pp Qq Rr Ss Tt Uu Vv Ww Xx Yy Zz

2 →

1 ↓

1 ↓
→ 2

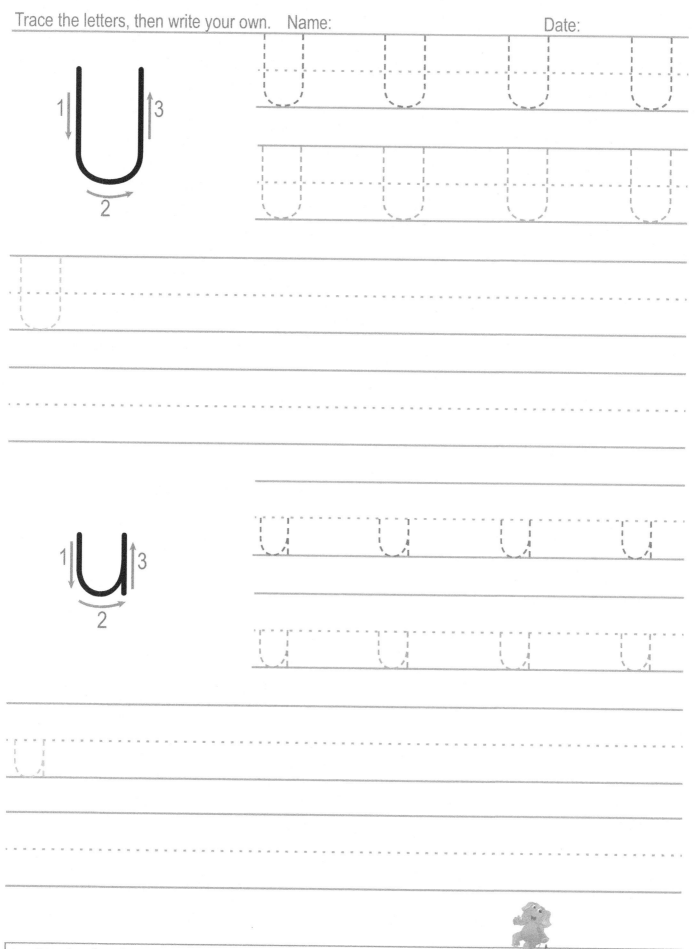

A a B b C c D d E e F f G g H h I i J j K k L l M m N n O o P p Q q R r S s T t U u V v W w X x Y y Z z

Aa Bb Cc Dd Ee Ff Gg Hh Ii Jj Kk Ll Mm Nn Oo Pp Qq Rr Ss Tt Uu Vv Ww Xx Yy Zz

W

W

Aa Bb Cc Dd Ee Ff Gg Hh Ii Jj Kk Ll Mm Nn Oo Pp Qq Rr Ss Tt Uu Vv Ww Xx Yy Zz

Trace the letters, then write your own.   Name: _____   Date: _____

Aa Bb Cc Dd Ee Ff Gg Hh Ii Jj Kk Ll Mm Nn Oo Pp Qq Rr Ss Tt Uu Vv Ww Xx Yy Zz

Z
1
2
3

Z
1
2
3

Aa Bb Cc Dd Ee Ff Gg Hh Ii Jj Kk Ll Mm Nn Oo Pp Qq Rr Ss Tt Uu Vv Ww Xx Yy Zz

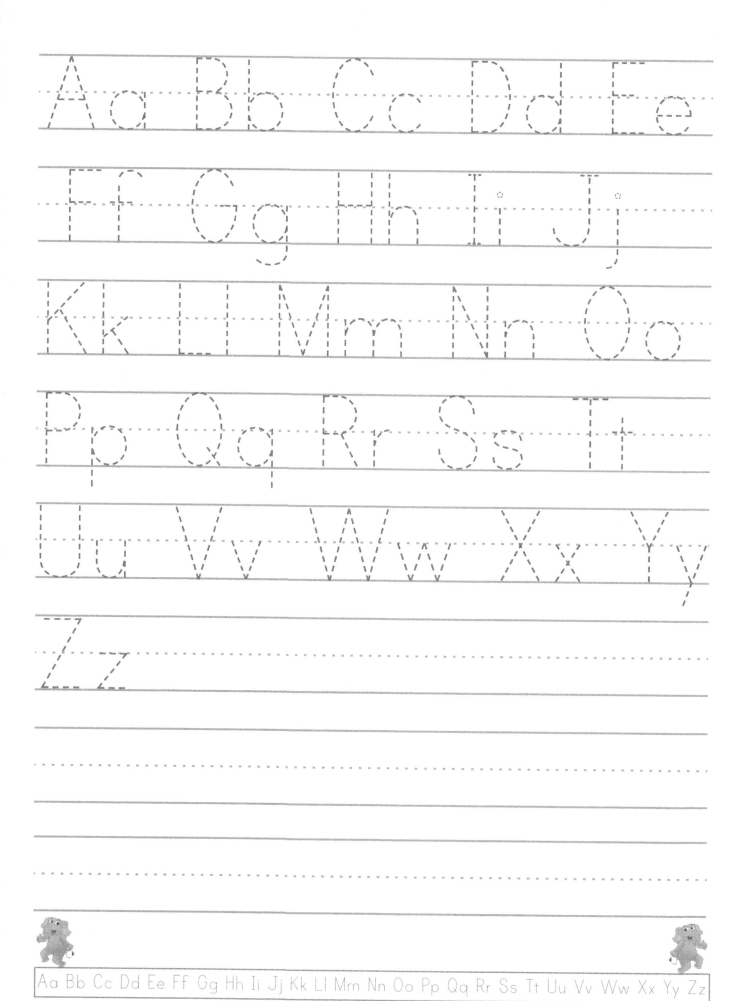

Aa Bb Cc Dd Ee Ff Gg Hh Ii Jj Kk Ll Mm Nn Oo Pp Qq Rr Ss Tt Uu Vv Ww Xx Yy Zz

Part 2:
Sight Words

Trace and learn four and five letter words

We will now practice writing words using a smaller letter size.

Trace the words and practice writing them in the remaining space!

*Note: We have skipped words beginning with the letter x

Great Going!

above   above   above

along   along   along

begin   begin   begin

below   below   below

carry   carry   carry

close   close   close

door   door   door

draw   draw   draw

earth   earth   earth

every   every   every

first   first   first

found found found

great   great   great

group   group   group

high   high   high

house house house

idea   idea   idea

into   into   into

job   job   job   job

jokes   jokes   jokes

kind   kind   kind

know   know   know

leave   leave   leave

live   live   live

might   might   might

must must must

never never never

night night night

only only only

open open open

paper   paper   paper

point   point   point

quest   quest   quest

quiz   quiz   quiz

real   real   real

right   right   right

school   school

sight   sight   sight

think   think   think

those those those

until   until   until

upon   upon   upon

very   very   very

voice   voice   voice

watch   watch   watch

world   world   world

year   year   year

your   your   your

zip   zip   zip

zone   zone   zone

Part 3:
Numbers and Number Words

We will now practice writing numbers
and number words from 1 - 100.

Trace the dotted numbers and number words,
then write them on your own
in the remaining space.

You are
AMAZING!

Name: Date:

11   11   11

12   12   12

13   13   13

14   14   14

15   15   15

16   16   16

17   17   17

18   18   18

19   19   19

20   20   20

21 21 21

22 22 22

23 23 23

24 24 24

25 25 25

26 26 26

27 27 27

28 28 28

29 29 29

30 30 30

31   31   31

32   32   32

33   33   33

34   34   34

35   35   35

36   36   36

37   37   37

38   38   38

39   39   39

40   40   40

1   1   1

2   2   2

3   3   3

4   4   4

5   5   5

6   6   6

7   7   7

8   8   8

9   9   9

0   0   0

51   52   53   54   55

56   57   58   59   60

61   62   63   64   65

66   67   68   69   70

71   72   73   74   75

76   77   78   79   80

81   82   83   84   85

86   87   88   89   90

91   92   93   94   95

96   97   98   99   100

one   one   one   one

two   two   two   two

three   three   three

four   four   four   four

five   five   five   five

six   six   six   six

seven   seven   seven

eight   eight   eight

nine   nine   nine   nine

ten   ten   ten   ten

eleven eleven eleven

twelve twelve twelve

thirteen thirteen

fourteen fourteen

fifteen fifteen

sixteen sixteen

seventeen seventeen

eighteen eighteen

nineteen nineteen

twenty twenty

twenty-one

twenty-two

twenty-three

twenty-four

twenty-five

twenty-six

twenty-seven

twenty-eight

twenty-nine

thirty

thirty-one

thirty-two

thirty-three

thirty-four

thirty-five

thirty-six

thirty-seven

thirty-eight

thirty-nine

forty

forty one

forty two

forty three

forty four

forty five

forty six

forty seven

forty eight

forty nine

fifty

fifty-one

fifty-two

fifty-three

fifty-four

fifty-five

fifty-six

fifty-seven

fifty-eight

fifty-nine

sixty

sixty-one

sixty-two

sixty-three

sixty-four

sixty-five

sixty-six

sixty-seven

sixty-eight

sixty-nine

seventy

seventy-one

seventy-two

seventy-three

seventy-four

seventy-five

seventy-six

seventy-seven

seventy-eight

seventy-nine

eighty

eighty-one

eighty-two

eighty-three

eighty-four

eighty-five

eighty-six

eighty-seven

eighty-eight

eighty-nine

ninety

ninety one

ninety two

ninety three

ninety four

ninety five

ninety six

ninety seven

ninety eight

ninety nine

one hundred

Part 4:
Knock Knock

We will now practice writing
sentences using a smaller letter size.

Trace the dotted knock knock jokes
and try telling them to your friends and family.

Use your best handwriting!

Knock, knock.

Who's there?

Baby owl.

Baby owl who?

Baby owl see you later,

maybe I won't!

Knock, knock.

Who's there?

Snow!

Snow who?

Snow skating today

the ice is too thin!

Knock, knock.

Who's there?

Pasture.

Pasture who?

Pasture bed time, isn't it?

Knock, knock.

Who's there?

Frank!

Frank who?

Frank who for being such

a great friend!

Knock, knock.

Who's there?

Justin.

Justin who?

Justin time for dinner.

Knock, knock.

Who's there?

Olive.

Olive who?

Olive you!

Knock, knock.

Who's there?

Norma Lee.

Norma Lee who?

Norma Lee I have my key,

can you let me in?

Knock, knock.

Who's there?

Pizza.

Pizza who?

Pizza really great guy!

Knock, knock.

Who's there?

Nuisance.

Nuisance who?

What's nuisance yesterday?

Knock, knock.

Who's there?

Doris.

Doris who?

Doris locked,

that's why I knocked.

Knock, knock.

Who's there?

Cash.

Cash who?

No thanks,

I'll have some peanuts.

Knock, knock.

Who's there?

Howard.

Howard who?

Howard I know?

Knock, knock.

Who's there?

Tank.

Tank who?

You're welcome.

Knock, knock.

Who's there?

Candice

Candice who?

Candice door open, or

what?

Knock, knock.

Who's there?

Dozen.

Dozen who?

Dozen anyone live here

anymore?

Knock, knock.

Who's there?

Owls say.

Owls say who?

Yes, they do.

Knock, knock.

Who's there?

Figs.

Figs who?

Figs your doorbell,

it's not working!

Knock, knock.

Who's there?

Mikey.

Mikey who?

Mikey doesn't fit in the

keyhole!

Knock, knock.

Who's there?

Lettuce.

Lettuce who?

Lettuce in,

it's cold out here!

Knock, knock.

Who's there?

Boo!

Boo who?

No need to cry,

it's only a joke.

Part 5:
Jokes

Trace the dotted jokes
and practice writing them on your own
in the remaining space.

Share the jokes with your friends and family
for more laughs!

Use your best handwriting!

You are
brilliant!

What's the difference
between a guitar
and a fish?
You can't tuna fish.

What does a nosey pepper
do?Gets jalapeno business!

What is it called when a
cat wins a dog show?
A CAT HAS TROPHY!

What is red and smells like
blue paint?
Red paint.

I'm friends with 25 letters

of the alphabet.

A B C D E F G H I
J K L M N O P Q R
S T U V W X ? Z

I don't know y.

What do you get from a

pampered cow?

Spoiled milk.

What do you call a fat

psychic?

A four chin teller.

What do you call an eleph

ant that doesn't

matter? An irrelephant.

Why did the belt get

arrested?

It held up a pair of pants.

What do you call a

computer that sings?

A Dell

Why did the banana go to
the doctor? Because
he wasn't peeling well.

Did you hear about the
angry pancake?
He just flipped.

What do you call a dinosaur
with an extensive
vocabulary?
A Thesaurus.

What is heavy forward but
not backward? Ton

What bow can't be tied?

A rainbow!

What goes through towns,

up and over hills,

but doesn't move?

The road!

What belongs to you but
others use more?
Your name.

Why did the birdie go to
the hospital?
To get a tweetment.

What do you call an
illegally parked frog?
Toad.

What stays in the corner
and travels all over the
world? A stamp!

Why did the picture go to

jail?

Because it was framed.

What's a computer's

favorite animal?

A mouse!

Who earns a living driving
their customers away?
A taxi driver.

Did you hear about the car
rot detective? He got
to the root of every case.

What do you call a man
with no body and
just a nose? Nobody nose.

What never asks questions
but is always answered?
The telephone.

What do you call a laughing
motorcycle? A Yamahahaha.

Did you hear about the
crab that went to
the seafood disco?
He pulled a mussel.

Why don't you see giraffes

in elementary school?

Because they're all in

High School!

What do you call sad

coffee? Despresso.

What goes up when the
rain comes down?
An umbrella.

What do you call a dentist
in the army?
A drill sergeant.

What do you call a funny
mountain?
Hilarious.

What's easy to get into but
hard to get out of?
Trouble.

What kind of shoes do spies wear? Sneakers.

Where does bad light go? PRISM.

Can February March? No. But April May.

How do spiders communi
cate? Through the
World Wide Web.

Why are chefs so mean?
They beat the eggs and
whip the cream.

What music are balloons
afraid of? Pop music.

What do you call a man
with a rubber toe? Roberto!

6/5 of people admit that
they're bad with fractions.

What's the advantage of
living in Switzerland? The
flag definitely is a big plus.

What do you call an
alligator in a vest?
An investigator!

I don't trust stairs. They're always up to something.

What does a house wear?

A dress.

How many pears grow on a tree? All of them.

What's brown and sticky?

A stick.

I would avoid the sushi if I

were you. It's a little fishy.

Why don't lobsters share?

They're SHELLFISH.

Why does Peter pan always fly? Because he neverlands!

What's orange and sounds like a parrot? A carrot!

How do you get Pikachu on a bus? You POKE-EM-ON

Why can't two elephants

go swimming?

Because they only

have one pair of trunks.

What rhymes with orange?

No it doesn't.

What do you call a group
of killer whales playing
instruments? An Orca-stra.

Why couldn't the bicycle
stand up by itself?
It was two tired.

Want to hear a joke about

construction?

I'm still working on it.

What kind of shoes does

a thief wear?

Sneakers.

There's a new type of
broom out, its's
sweeping the nation.

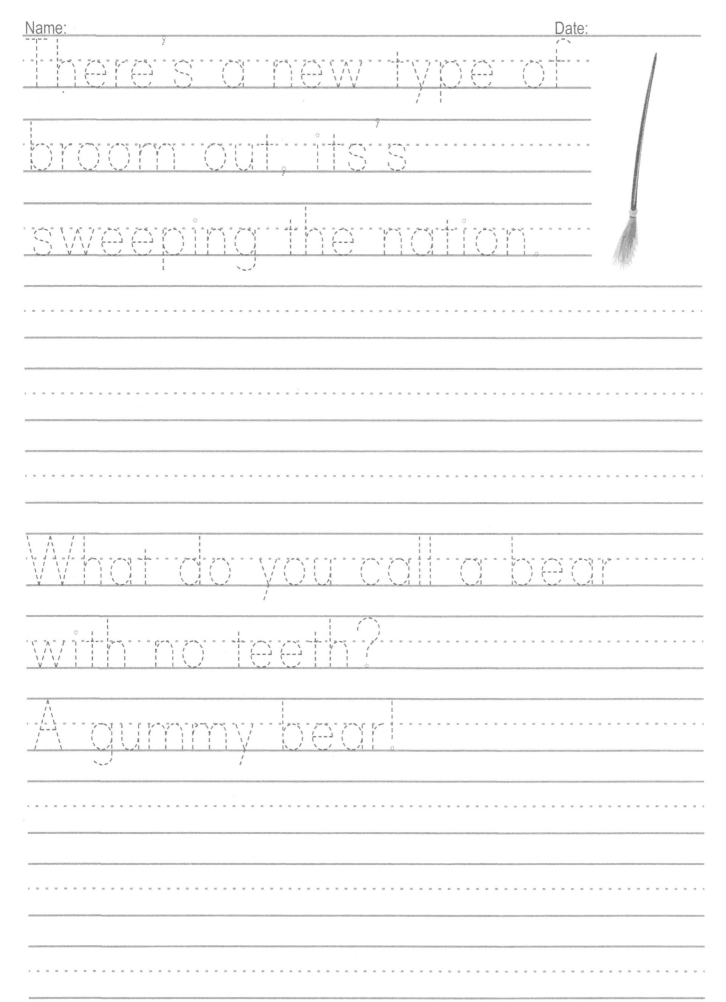

What do you call a bear
with no teeth?
A gummy bear!

Want to hear a pizza joke?

Noh, it's too cheesy!

Why was 6 afraid of 7?

Because 7, 8, 9.

What do elves learn in

school? The elf-abet.

How do you make a tissue dance? You put a little boogie in it.

Why couldn't the pony sing himself a lullaby?

He was a little hoarse.

What did the triangle say to the circle? You're pointless!

What do you call a horse that lives next door? A neighbor!

What do you call a pile of
kittens? A meowntain

What do lawyers wear to
court? Lawsuits!

How do you organize a
a space party? You planet!

Why did the thief take a bath? Because he wanted to make a clean getaway.

Why did the baby straw-berry cry? Because his parents were in a jam!

What do you call a bear

with no socks on?

Bare foot.

Why was the math book

sad? Because it had too

many problems.